U H Univ

The making of
modern malnutrition

An overview of food poverty in the UK

THE CAROLINE WALKER
LECTURE 1996

Suzi Leather

THE CAROLINE WALKER TRUST

© Suzi Leather 1996
Four diagrams on pages 33-35
by Suzi Leather and Michael Nelson

Caroline Walker Trust
22 Kindersley Way
Abbots Langley
Herts   WD5 0DQ

Registered Charity 328580

Printed by KKS PRINTING
Edited by David Dickinson
Charts and graphs designed by
Helen Dyer and Nancy Yuill

ISBN 1 897820 05 4

Suzi Leather

Suzi Leather has worked in consumer representation since 1978, variously as a senior research officer with the Consumers in Europe Group, the Consumer Panel of the Ministry of Agriculture Fisheries and Food, the Nutrition Task Force's project team on food for those with a low income, the National Consumer Council, the National Food Alliance – and many other groups and committees in the UK and Europe.

Her special interests include consumers with low incomes, the links between nutrition and poverty and the impact of European policies on consumers. Her work in unearthing the hazards of organophosphorus sheep dips was especially and widely admired; for that and her other work on the MAFF Consumer Panel, she won the Caroline Walker Trust's Consumer Award in 1993. For services to agriculture and food safety, she was awarded an MBE in 1994.

As well as an accomplished writer and broadcaster on food and food policy, Suzi Leather is an honorary research fellow and part-time lecturer at the University of Exeter. She also works as a consultant on consumer issues. She lives in Exeter and is married with three children.

The Caroline Walker Trust

The Trust was set up in memory of the nutritionist and campaigner Caroline Walker, who died in 1988. The Trust's mission is the improvement of public health by means of good food – a cause which Caroline made important to everybody in this country. The Trust, which relies on charitable donations, exists to further her work through research and publications.

A note about the text

As the written version of a spoken lecture, the organisation of the text needs a few words of explanation. The opposite page summarises my recommendations to fight food poverty: ten commandments which follow from the arguments I have put forward in the rest of the paper. The supporting arguments and fuller versions of the recommendations can be found towards the end of the text.

The main text is divided into four parts. First is a brief introduction. Then there is an historical account of food insecurity and what helped to end it. Next, I consider modern malnutrition: how it emerged, its distinct character and causes. Lastly I consider the options for tackling food poverty. I argue that modern food poverty is in some ways dissimilar from historical food insecurity. In particular, there has been a shift from concern with getting enough calories to a concern with specific nutrients. As our calorie requirements have dropped due to our less active life-style, the quality of the diet in terms of nutrient density has become more important. In short, the debate is now less about food quantity than food quality.

There has also been a shift from the almost exclusive concern about the material aspects of poverty to the more social (or psychosocial) effects. Modern analyses of poverty often take account of social exclusion which is highly relevant to any consideration of food poverty. Food is of course much more than a vehicle for nutrients. Food choice is an expression of the belonging aspects of our lives: family habits, regional identity, national, religious and cultural traditions.

Ten recommendations to combat food poverty

1 People have a right to an adequate supply of food. Government policy should be to recognise this right in law; to guarantee an income adequate to meet basic food needs; and to ensure easy access to and diversity of choice in local shopping facilities in deprived areas.

2 Benefits should once again be uprated in line with average earnings, rather than with prices at present, and benefits should cover basic needs including the cost of a healthy diet.

3 Grants, not loans, should be made for the purchase of essential equipment such as cookers and fridges.

4 Increased allowances need to be made against earnings, child benefit, and maintenance payment when calculating benefit levels.

5 Income support should be reinstated for 16 and 17-year-olds.

6 We must have a safety net for children at nutritional risk, including at least one nutritionally adequate meal a day, in term time and holidays; nutritional standards for school meals in law; school breakfasts, free school milk, free school fruit and free school meals in areas of need; and a programme to help prevent underweight babies.

7 Cooking skills should be part of the National Curriculum at all ages.

8 More older people should be eligible for meals on wheels. Shopping-carrying schemes are needed to allow older people to remain in their homes and live independently.

9 Low-cost food shopping has to be encouraged, by the encouragement of street markets; by extending the range of 'value' lines in supermarkets, and including fresh fruit and vegetables; by creating a map of 'shopping deserts' and requiring local authorities and retailers to set up there.

10 Local authorities should be required to support community food projects, and where possible to make home delivery services, tele-shopping, distance shopping available to low-income consumers.

Caroline Walker and food poverty

Most of us, George Eliot wrote in Middlemarch, live 'faithfully a hidden life, and rest in unvisited tombs.'[1] Not so Caroline Walker. That her tomb is visited, albeit metaphorically; that her life remains a public one, celebrated by this annual event and by the Caroline Walker Trust, is due to the love she inspired during that life. A love quickened by her courage, humour and applied intelligence.

Caroline chose to apply her intelligence to the area she felt mattered more than any other: to good health through whole fresh food. Her remarkable achievements are recognized. What is perhaps less widely known is that in her early nutritional research, the food issue that set her on her campaigning path was what has come to be called 'food poverty'.

In 1978 Caroline completed her studies for her MSc in Human Nutrition with the highest marks ever achieved in the examinations. Her thesis subject was *'Single-Parent Families and Social Insecurity'*, upon which she wrote her first scientific article entitled *'Poverty by Administration'*.[2] She later became nutrition adviser to the Child Poverty Action Group. It is particularly fitting therefore that this year the lecture given in her name should be about food poverty.

Although Caroline was fortunate by birth (she attended Cheltenham Ladies College), and never herself experienced the suffering that poverty imposes, she was very keen to document and publicize the effect of inadequate income on diet. She was a good citizen of the kind described by William Beveridge – founder of our welfare state – when he wrote to his mother from Toynbee Hall in 1904, 'No man can really be a good citizen who goes through life in a watertight compartment of his own class.'

Professor Philip James, in giving Caroline's funeral address, quoted a Quaker saying:

> 'Only such writings as spring from the living experience will reach into the life of others.'[3]

Acknowledging that truth, I have tried to balance analysis with material which conveys something of the texture and reality of modern food poverty. In the course of preparing this lecture, I interviewed many people experiencing food poverty. I quote many of them in the text. Their words – stark, raw, persuasive – should help us all to move out of our class compartments, and to be good citizens in the face of a profound and deeply damaging social injustice.

A history of food shortages

Food security has been achieved in our country only in comparatively recent times. Insecurity of food supplies, 'the rhythm of the seasons and the hazards of the harvest',[4] impinged historically on both the highest and lowest orders – although unsurprisingly, it always bore down most heavily on the poor.

Throughout most of our history there have been very great social inequalities in 'the distribution of nourishment'.[5] We have only, even in times of plenty, to think back to the vast magnificence of the medieval baronial hall compared with the peasant's lot. For much of the medieval and early modern period, the upper classes ate a far larger proportion of meat than poorer people. Gross inequalities in nourishment diminished only gradually, and fluctuated according to economic conditions.

Throughout the medieval and early modern period subsistence crises were very frequent. In England, in the period 1500-1660, about one harvest in six appears to have been a serious failure.[6] The direct relationship between harvest failures and soaring death rates only gradually unravelled in western Europe – from the late seventeenth century onwards, thanks to improvements in trade and transport. In the late seventeenth and early eighteenth centuries, England began to enjoy greater security of food supply and a more equitable social distribution of food. Even so, high food prices following crop failures were still associated with raised death rates in years of bad harvests in the 1720s and 1740s.

Insecurity caused by harvest failure began to be replaced by insecurity caused by market fluctuations associated with trade patterns. 'The growth in trade, if it enabled the surplus of one region rather more often than before to relieve the dearth of another, also left a larger number of people at the mercy of market fluctuation, tended to depress or hold down real wages, and increase the gap between the rich and the poor.'[7] Food riots were still common in eighteenth century England and there was still a pervasive fear of hunger, particularly among poorer people, right into the late nineteenth century.

Documenting the inequalities

From the 1860s onwards, surveys documented very large differences in diet between rich and poor. In early modern times, dietary differences are thought to have been greatest between 1880 and 1890, when the diets of the poor were probably furthest from nutritional adequacy.[8] Rowntree's seminal studies in York in 1900 indicate very significant differences in calorie intake between different classes: poor families consumed only 1,659 kcal per person per day; average working-class families, the figure was 2,378 kcal; and 2,754 kcal in the 'servant-keeping' class.[9]

Rowntree's studies also showed significant differences in actual amounts of foods consumed: the poor ate only 3 ounces of currants and jam (and almost no fresh fruit) per person per week; the rich consumed up to 30 ounces, and also enjoyed fresh fruit. Today, the consumption of fresh fruit is still a powerful indicator of income difference, with rich families consuming two or three times more than poor families.[10]

Using food to measure poverty

So intimate was the relationship between poverty and hunger (or grossly inadequate diet), that in the late nineteenth century attempts were made to calculate the scale of the poverty problem by using measurements of dietary adequacy. Charles Booth's survey of London's East End in 1886 found that 31 per cent of the population lived in abject poverty. His work stimulated Benjamin Seebohm Rowntree to conduct a house-to-house study of the whole of the wage-earning population of York in 1899. He found that 9.9 per cent of the population were living in what he called 'primary poverty' and 18 per cent in 'secondary poverty'. In other words, 28 per cent of the population could not afford the 3,500 calories a day necessary for a man in moderate work. By the mid 1930s the situation had improved somewhat: Rowntree found that the numbers living in poverty had dropped to 18 per cent in 1936.[11]

In 1913, Maud Pember Reeves' book 'Round About a Pound a Week' made a remarkable impact. Pember Reeves and other members of the

Fabian Women's Group recorded the daily budgets and daily lives of working-class families in Lambeth. The book was less rigorously scientific than its predecessors, but nonetheless persuasive. It was a time of national concern about the nation's physical and economic deterioration. Recruitment for the disastrous Boer War had shown that nearly half of working-class army volunteers in industrial towns were undersized or suffering from physical defects or active disease.[12] *Round About a Pound a Week* showed how 'at once independent, resourceful, hardworking respectable' working-class mothers were bringing up their families on wholly inadequate incomes. Pember Reeves presented to a largely ignorant public the realities of poverty. 'The conclusions were inescapable – the cause of infant mortality was not that mothers were ignorant or degenerate, but that they had too little money to provide for their own and their families' essential needs; they lacked decent housing, domestic equipment, adequate food and clothing, and any facilities or opportunities for recreation.'[13]

The connections between poverty and poor diet were neatly drawn by Boyd Orr who showed in the mid-1930s that malnutrition – that is to say, dietary inadequacy – increased as income fell. He also showed that diets became inadequate when food expenditure fell below 8 shillings or about 40p per person, per week.[14]

How wars improved the diets of poor people

Mechanisms to end food poverty were put in place when there was the political will. Put cynically, the need for fit cannon fodder for two world wars focussed politician's minds wonderfully. Anxiety about the physical state of the nation, and the difficulty of recruiting enough able-bodied men for the Boer War, led to the social reforms of the Liberal Government, including the 1906 Education (Provision of Meals) Act. This introduced the school meal service by allowing local authorities to levy a rate of a halfpenny in the pound to provide meals for 'children unable by reason of lack of food to take full advantage of the education provided to them.'

Fuelled by studies such as Rowntree's, Booth's and Pember Reeves', there was an active debate in the 1930s on malnutrition and a series of social reforms designed to improve the nutrition of the poor were adopted. A 'Milk in Schools' scheme was started by the Milk Marketing Board and Board of Education in 1934, supplying a third of a pint of milk daily to needy elementary school children, at half cost or free.[15] In 1939 research was published confirming that school milk benefitted not only children's health but also contributed to their educational achievements.[16] Also by 1939, health departments were providing free or low-cost milk, cod liver oil, iron, and vitamins to mothers and children with signs of malnutrition.

During the Second World War a National Milk Scheme allowed seven pints of free or cheap milk a week to all children under 5 years. In 1946, the school milk scheme was extended to pupils under 18 in all schools. By the end of the war, there were school meals for all, with government grants to education authorities covering 95 per cent of the cost. Nutritional standards were set in 1941. Eggs were available to mothers and expectant mothers. All these measures 'not only protected the nutrition of vulnerable groups but also had the positive effect of rectifying deficient nutritional status for the poorest families which had been present during the pre-war years.'[17] In the war, said the government, 'the average diet of all classes was better balanced than ever before. Luxury items soon disappeared, it is true, and meals tended to become monotonous, particularly in 1941 when the U-boat campaign was at its height, but it was nevertheless, always physiologically a better diet and more evenly distributed.'[18]

What really ended food insecurity?

Historically, food insecurity began as a production problem, and then became a problem of distribution – whether caused by market fluctuation or by inequality of income. Food insecurity was ended by production developments; by increasing economic equality; and by benefits which were targeted at the nutritionally insecure.

Production problems were eased by the development of more productive agricultural methods and new ways to preserve food. Refrigeration and canning benefited the entire population. International food trade brought out-of-season produce, and helped to spread the risk of poor harvests over a much larger geographical area, easing problems of market fluctuation.

It was rationing that fundamentally changed the income-related inequalities of food distribution in the UK.[19] But we shouldn't underestimate the importance of increased economic equality. A long-term trend towards income equality can be traced back to the fifteenth century[20] – but the momentum was greatest in this century, and accelerated between the 1930s and the late 1970s. This allowed a narrowing of food inequality to continue long after the end of rationing. The trend was abruptly reversed with the unleashing of the Thatcher revolution. As we shall see, this had profound consequences for the food choices of the poor.

The 1970s: food poverty returns

Given the lessons of historical analysis, what factors were needed to encourage the re-emergence of food poverty? The most obvious background conditions would be a growth in overall poverty and at the same time a widening gap between the incomes of the best and worst off. And this is precisely what happened from the end of the 1970s.

The growth of the income gap

The increase in income inequality – 'unprecedented in social history this century' [21] – sharply reversed the long-term trend towards income equality. While the richest got richer, the incomes of the poorest sections of the population actually fell. The average household's real income rose by 36 per cent after housing costs between 1979 and 1990/91. But the real income of the richest ten per cent of the population rose by 62%, while the income of the poorest ten per cent fell by 14 per cent (see chart, page 14).

Let's put it in terms of actual money. 'The real incomes of the poorest tenth ranked by income after housing costs actually fell sharply from a peak in 1979 of £73 per week to just over £61 per week.' [22,23] The numbers of people living in poverty (defined by the EU and OECD as less than half of average household income) rose from 5 million in 1979 to 14.1 million in 1992/93 – one quarter of the population. [24]

Benefit poverty: Robin Hood changes sides

The predominant immediate cause of the increase in poverty was of course unemployment. But taxation and benefit changes were highly significant. Until 1980 there was a link between benefits and average earnings, which effectively meant that the income of people on benefit increased in line with the incomes of those in work. In 1980, the link was broken, and

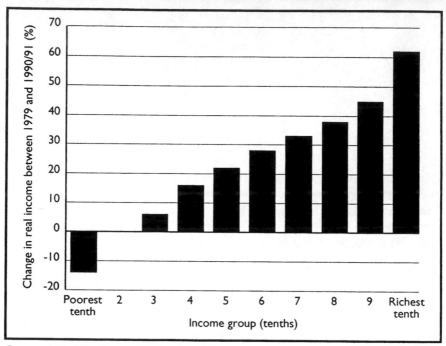

Income changes 1979-90: poor people get poorer

Change in real income between 1979 and 1990/91 (%)

Income group (tenths): Poorest tenth, 2, 3, 4, 5, 6, 7, 8, 9, Richest tenth

Source: Hills, J, *The Future of Welfare*, Joseph Rowntree Foundation, York, 1993

benefits linked to prices. People who were earning began to enjoy more prosperity, as their earnings rose by more than prices. People on benefit did not. This policy inevitably opened up a gap in living standards between those on benefits and those on average earnings.

At the same time, a trend away from direct taxation (eg income tax) towards indirect taxation (such as VAT on a widening range of goods and services), meant that the poor actually began to pay *more* of their income in tax than the rich. In 1979, the poorest fifth of households paid less tax than the richest fifth – 31 per cent of their gross income, compared with 37 per cent for the rich. By 1991, the poorest fifth paid 38 per cent of their incomes on tax, compared with 34 per cent for the richest fifth. 'Robin Hood has changed sides' said one trade union report.[25]

Changes to social security in 1988 made almost half the poorest 20 per

Change in income inequality: UK is second worst

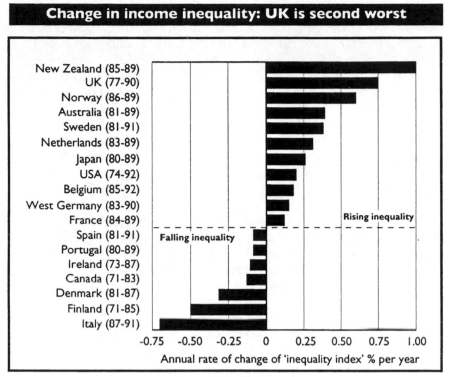

Source: Income and Wealth Inquiry Group chaired by Sir Peter Barclay, *Inquiry into Income and Wealth*, Joseph Rowntree Foundation, York, 1995

cent of households worse off.[26] The poor suffered falls in real income at a time when their other costs were rising: a recent report by the Institute for Fiscal Studies found that while the average income of council tenants was a fifth lower than it had been 20 years before, rents had doubled in real terms since 1979.[27]

Trends reversed; inequalities re-established

By the mid-1980s the share of after-tax income taken by the richest people was higher than at any time since the Second World War[28]. The level of inequality reached by 1990 was almost back to 1930 levels estimated by the Royal Commission on the Distribution of Income and Wealth 1938.[29] Among industrialised nations, the UK was exceptional in the pace and extent of the increase in inequality in the 1980s. Only New Zealand in 1985-89 showed a faster rate of increase (see chart, above).

One in four children under the European poverty line

Caroline Walker was especially concerned in her work about children living in poverty. Her concern would be all the greater today, when nearly 4 million British children live in families with incomes below 50 per cent of average earnings – up from 1.4 million in 1979. In today's money, less than half average earnings is about £115 a week. Depending on the ages of the children and the number of adults in the family, many households on benefit have a maximum income less than this amount (see table of Benefit rates, page 27). Today one British child in four is being brought up in a family living on means-tested benefits like Income Support or Family Credit. In a class of 40 kids you can expect 10 of them, on average, to be living on benefit.

In 1979 fewer than one in 12 families had no working members. Today the figure is one in five. Many of those in work earn too little to be able to support a family. In 1993 researchers at Liverpool repeated Rowntree's approach to calculating the percentage of the population living in poverty and concluded 'we can safely say that at least 30 per cent of families with two children are living on or below a primary poverty line.'[30]

Given the sheer scale of this epidemic of poverty, it's barely surprising that food poverty once more emerged to ravage the most vulnerable.

Holes in the nutritional safety net

Between the 1930s and the 1970s little work was done on food security. Perhaps everyone assumed that – with the advance of the modern welfare state – the social evils identified by Beveridge in the 1940s (want, ignorance, disease, squalor and idleness) had disappeared, and that malnutrition had gone with them. The introduction of a rigorous rationing system, welfare foods (such as the National Milk Scheme for pregnant women and young children in 1940), and a marked reduction in income inequalities, were certainly significant factors in the trend towards a more equitable distribution of food. It might have looked as if we had solved the problems of nutrition for good. Events proved otherwise.

Caroline Walker's MSc thesis and article in 1978 drew attention to the inadequacy of state benefits by demonstrating that the supplementary benefit allowance was inadequate to cover the food needs of the largest 8 to 10 year-olds, even with the most 'efficient' purchasing patterns.[31] Michael Nelson's research (1979) neatly showed the correlation between restrictions on income or low amounts spent per person per week on food and poor growth in children. That poverty stunted children must have been widely observed, but neither the origin nor the scale of the problem was recognized. In fact eleven per cent of the children in the Nelson survey were mildly to moderately malnourished – and this was when the mesh of the nutritional safety net was still fine in comparison with today.[32]

Official recognition of the importance of the nutritional safety net could have come from the working group set up by the last Labour administration, under Sir Douglas Black, to consider inequalities in health. But, shamefully, the incoming Conservative government never properly printed and published the Black report (1980). Instead, only a few duplicated copies of the typescript were made available to selected journalists on the Friday before the August Bank Holiday.[33] Perhaps this was because Black concluded that the predominant explanation for health inequalities lay in material deprivation. Black had also indicated that there was under-nutrition and stunted growth amongst poor school children, which would increase if the provision of school meals and milk was not extended in the poorest sections of the community. 'In our view any reduction in the provision of school meals, or in eligibility for free meals, would mean putting further at risk the development of significant numbers of children' said the report.[34]

Research shows food poverty on the prowl again

Through the 1980s and into the 1990s research into food poverty continued, carried out by independent charities and concerned researchers. The effects of the recession on diet and health in the north of England was documented in the seminal study *Jam Tomorrow* (1984). Much of the evidence in that report has now become depressingly familiar: people missing meals, cutting back on food when short of cash, inadequate diets despite people making food a priority.[35] In the same year, the Maternity Alliance published *'Poverty in Pregnancy'*, on the cost of an adequate diet in pregnancy. It found that 'women on supplementary benefit, in particular, urgently need help if they are to be properly nourished and their own health and that of their babies is to be protected.'[36]

'Tightening Belts' (1986), published by the London Food Commission surveyed the food poverty problem, including the effect of proposed changes in social security and education legislation, and called for a wealth of reforms.[37] There was acute concern among poverty researchers that reforms in the welfare state were seriously affecting the nutritional health of the poorest people. This was despite an extraordinary claim by the then

Secretary of State for Health and Social Security, John Moore, that what
he called 'real poverty' had been abolished in the UK by the government's
'economic success'.[38]

No 'real poverty' in the UK...

It was hard to square John Moore's claims with the shocking findings of
the NCH Poverty and Nutrition Survey (1991). A survey of families
attending NCH family centres found that:

- 20 per cent of parents and 10 per cent of children had gone hungry in
  the month before the survey because, they said, they did not have
  enough money to buy food
- two-thirds of the children and over half the parents were eating
  nutritionally poor diets
- nearly half of the parents had gone short of food in the past year in
  order to ensure other family members had enough
- average food expenditure was under £10 per person per week at a time
  when the national average was £12.69.

Two years later, in a 1993 survey on debt problems faced by low income
families on benefits and low wages, NCH found that:[39]

- 50 per cent had to borrow money in order to buy basic necessities
  including food
- over two-thirds said there were times when they did not have enough
  money to buy the food their families needed
- nearly half of those with earned incomes sometimes did not have
  enough money to eat
- average weekly spending on food was only £9.10 per person – but this
  was a third of their total income
- 34 per cent said they were unable to eat properly because of financial
  worries.

Spending on food in poor familes*	
Family size	**Spending (£)**
TWO ADULTS AND ONE CHILD	
per person per week	9.79
per person per day	1.39
LONE PARENT FAMILIES	
per person per week	9.96
per person per day	1.42

* income group D/E2   **Source:** National Food Survey, 1993

Surveys like these NCH ones are sometimes criticised, particularly by government, as being small scale and unrepresentative. In fact, the government's own food survey data confirms these low levels of food expenditure found by NCH (see table, page 18).

When you can't afford a healthy diet

The 1991 NCH survey also showed the added costs of eating healthily. Research by another group, the Family Budget Unit, found that households at the lowest levels of income would be unlikely to be able to afford a healthy diet in the normal range of food choice. Benefits simply weren't up to it. Their concept of a healthy diet which was 'modest but adequate' was also outside the reach of some. The Unit found that food expenditure needed to be increased by 6%-13 per cent in order to meet Department of Health recommendations for a healthy diet.[40]

The obvious conclusion from all this work was that food poverty had returned to haunt British society. It may not have been the acute calorie deficiency of other times or the starvation of other countries. Poor Britons were not moving with the awful languor characteristic of starvation and semi-starvation; our children were not turning up to school with Kwashiorkor. But the low quality of the diet was fundamentally undermining health.

No evidence of a problem...

Yet there was never any official response other than denial that there was a problem. In this culture of denial the government-funded Health Education Authority in 1988 suppressed a report it had itself commissioned on food poverty.[41] The trouble was that the kind of proposals recommended in the Black and other reports arguing the need for a nutritional safety net and adequate benefits, 'clashed resoundingly with Thatcherism', a philosophy which sought above all to reduce what it saw as 'the dependency culture'.[42] The link between poverty and ill health was persistently denied under Margaret Thatcher's leadership, and continues to be denied by ministers today.[43] Any report which recorded class divisions or made the links between poverty and ill health – even the Church of England's *Faith in the City* report – was dubbed Marxist by government ministers.

Despite the growth in poverty and a huge gap opening up between rich and poor, the government argued that since the real price of food had fallen, even the food purchasing power of the worst off must have improved. The government always made the general claim about the adequate purchasing power of benefits. In reply to a questions I raised and a paper written for the MAFF Consumer Panel[44], MAFF even attempted to

The ingredients of a 'low-cost healthy' diet*

Type of food	Daily amount (g)	Equivalent helping
Cheese	4	less than a quarter slice of processed cheese
Carcase meat	20	less than the edible portion of a chicken wing
Other meat products	17	less than a rasher of streaky bacon
Fish	13	less than half the fish in a fish finger
Eggs	5	less than an egg per week
Whole milk	0.29 pint	about half a cup
Skimmed milk	0.18 pint	about a third of a cup
Butter/margarine	19	almost enough for three slices of bread thinly spread
Other fats and oils	17	less than two tablespoons
Sugar	29	seven level teaspoons
Preserves	4	half a level teaspoon of jam
Potatoes	177	a medium-sized baked potato in its jacket
Fresh green vegetables	46	less than a small portion of boiled cabbage
Other green vegetables	66	one and a half medium boiled carrots
Canned beans	49	a tablespoon of baked beans
Frozen vegetables	57	a medium-sized portion of peas
Other processed vegetables	41	a heaped tablespoon of sweetcorn
Fresh fruit	85	1/10 average glass of juice
Fruit juice	23	a small apple
Other fruit products	22	less than a fifth of an average portion of of tinned fruit
Cakes, buns and biscuits	9	a rich tea biscuit
Breakfast cereals	37	a medium-sized average portion of cornflakes
Wholemeal bread	48	two slices of a small loaf
Other bread	149	six slices of a small white loaf
Other cereal products	71	an average portion of cooked pasta
Beverages	16	enough tea, coffee or drinking chocolate to make several cups

Costing £10 per person per week in 1991
Source: Ministry of Agriculture, Fisheries and Food, 'The cost of alternative diets', Consumer Panel paper, 1992. The helping sizes based on H. Crawley, *Food Portion Sizes*, HMSO, 1990.

prove that food poverty could not exist by drawing up a 'low cost' healthy diet for £10 per person per week.[45]

The £10 a week diet was rapidly and easily dismissed. The diet proposed:
- cutting out meat almost entirely
- more than doubling the consumption of tinned fruit and frozen vegetables (an implicit recognition that the poor could not afford enough fresh fruit and vegetables)
- doubling consumption of breakfast cereals (in order to increase fibre and reliance on fortified vitamins)
- eating five times more wholemeal bread and more white bread
- completely excluding yogurts and other dairy products
- more than half the eight rounds of bread were to be eaten dry without even a thin spread of butter or margarine.[46]

The MAFF £10 healthy diet was actually tried for a week by some journalists and community groups including the Drumchapel Food Action Group. Apart from the difficulties of buying small quantities of some of the foods, they found the poor choice of foods unacceptable – and it was still not affordable. It was found to take up between 30 and 40 per cent of the income of families on benefit.[47] A somewhat similar exercise by Sainsbury's to design an affordable low-cost healthy diet also demonstrated the difficulty of eating healthily on a low income: the Sainsbury's low cost healthy diet took up more than 40 per cent of the income of a family living on benefit.[48] That proportion is unsustainable.

The poor pay more for their food

It is certainly true that food has become cheaper in real terms in the UK. The average proportion of income spent on household food has decreased steadily from just over 30 per cent in 1940 to only 12 per cent now.[49]

The present average of 12 per cent means that, as a nation, we devote less of our income to food than any other EU country.[50] But the proportion spent on food by the poor is far higher. The poorest fifth of the population spend 25 per cent of their total income on food. But as MAFF's research found out, to purchase a healthy diet would cost in excess of 30 per cent. It has been accepted as a rule of thumb, since Engel's work in the 19th century, that anyone who is spending more than 30 per cent of their income on food is living in poverty. Even today that figure is the foundation upon which the free-market, capitalist USA base its official definition of the poverty line.

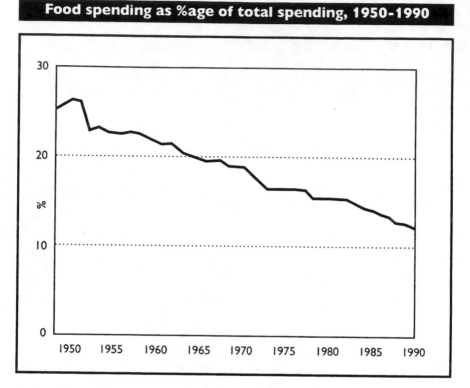

Food spending as %age of total spending, 1950-1990

Source: Central Statistical Office, *United Kingdom National Accounts, 1991*

Cheap food that is still out of reach

Food has got cheaper. MAFF has calculated how the real price of different meats has fallen, for instance, over the thirty years between 1960 and 1991. Allowing for the effects of inflation, pork fell in price by 31 per cent, poultry by 47 per cent and eggs by 53 per cent. We are faced with bewildering contradictions: so-called 'cheap' food co-existing with people who can't afford to eat properly.

As with taxes and general prosperity, however, so with food. There is also evidence that the rich have benefited more from food price falls than the poor. Leafy salads and fresh tomatoes, foods chosen by the better-off, fell in price by 24 per cent and 36 per cent respectively between 1960 and 1992. Cabbages and onions, foods eaten more by the poor, actually went up in real terms over the same period – by 0.4 per cent and 17 per cent.[51]

Despite spending a far higher proportion of their income on food than those on average or higher incomes, low-income families are unable to manage to purchase an adequate diet. It's often put about that people with little money spend it badly, as if they liked eating diets that undermined their health. In fact, low-income groups actually spend a *greater* proportion of their food money buying fresh fruit, potatoes and other vegetables than higher income groups do; the same is true of bread, rice and pasta.[52] So much for the behaviouralist idea that the poor have inadequate diets because they choose to – a myth which was in circulation in the 1930s and still surfaces today.

My historical review has demonstrated that the factors ensuring food security were not simply advances in agricultural production methods, or even the so-called cheap food policies, so much as policies which guaranteed equality of income and a nutritional safety net: notably, real

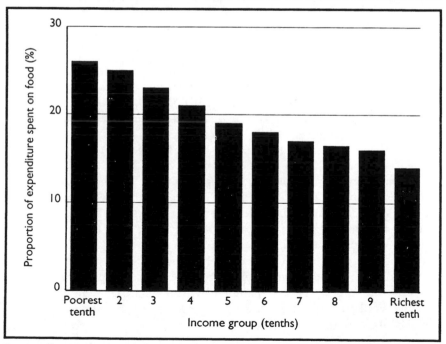

Percentage of expenditure on food by income decile group

Source: Central Statistical Office, *Family Spending. A Report of the 1994-95 Family Expenditure Survey*, HMSO, London, 1995

increases in wages and benefits and the setting up of such schemes as free school meals and free foods for those in need. We noted that for such policies to be put in place, there had to be official recognition of a nutritional problem. Problems of income equality and a safety net are also crucial to understanding modern malnutrition. Ironically, the success of food production methods and the intensification of production – our so-called cheap food economy – have not prevented the emergence of modern malnutrition. They lulled us into a false sense of security. We may be approaching the next millennium, but our social divisions now are reminiscent of the 1930s. The 'cheap food' economy mocks the experience of many millions who struggle to put food on their tables. It is the perfect foil for those who wish to deny that Britain has a food poverty problem.

The official response: Yes, we have no poverty

> 'To use the word poverty about the state in which some people are living is to make a moral judgment – and, implicitly at least, to call for something to be done. This is why there is such controversy about the definition of "poverty".'
> Fran Bennet, formerly Director of Child Poverty Action Group

> 'Expenditure preferences vary considerably, as does professional opinion on the diet question. Advice from the Department of Health is that the range of foodstuffs available at affordable prices is so wide that a healthy diet is available within anyone's means.'
> Department of Social Security Press Office, 17 October 1995.

Figures on the growth in numbers of people living on less than half average household earnings are official. They cannot be challenged *per se*, but their significance is disputed. Ministers have variously claimed that poverty has been eradicated in Britain. Most recently, Peter Lilley, writing to the UK International Year of the Eradication of Poverty Coalition, said that eradication plans recommended by the United Nations are not needed in the UK, 'which already has the infrastructure and social protection systems to prevent poverty and maintain living standards.' At an official level, the word poverty itself is banned, replaced by the banal and infinitely more soothing 'low income'.

I am reminded of the children's book *'There Is No Such Thing As A Dragon'*.[53] It is about a little dragon, who turns up on Billy Bixbee's bed one morning. Billy can see him but his mother, who does not believe in dragons, can't. As she explains, you cannot see what does not exist. But while it is ignored, the dragon grows: it turns into a much bigger dragon; it first threatens and then succeeds in destroying the Bixbee house. The destruction wrought by the dragon forces Billy's parents to acknowledge its existence; the dragon, satisfied, shrinks. 'Why did it have to grow so big?' asks Billy's mother. 'I'm not sure, but I think it just wanted to be noticed' says the wise Billy Bixbee.

Denial tempered with buck-passing

At an official level, the response to the crisis of food poverty has been denial tempered with buck-passing. MAFF says 'The term food poverty does not really have a definition. If the question is should people have enough money to eat properly, it is a matter for the Department of Social Security.'[54] The Department of Health says 'For food poverty you should speak to the Department of Social Security'.[55] The DSS says 'The Government is not in the business of working out what you can buy with Income Support. The policy is that you can buy a healthy diet within the current benefit rates.'[56]

John Beaumont, chief executive of the food retailers' Institute of Grocery Distribution, is more realistic when he says *'For the majority of households in the United Kingdom the provision of food is not problematical. However there exists a minority of households and individuals whose income is so low that the purchase of an adequate food supply is a problem. For many there is a question mark over their nutritional security.'*[57] The current benefit rates are as follows:

Total benefits for families on Income Support, 1996-97				
Household type	Total weekly income (£)		Total annual income (£)	
	per family	per person	per family	per person
Couple with two children under 11	100.65	25.16	5233.80	1308.45
Lone parent with two children under 11	96.55	24.13	5020.60	1255.15
Couple with two children 11-15	115.95	28.98	6029.40	1507.35
Lone parent with two children 11-15	111.85	27.96	5816.20	1454.05

Source: Child Poverty Action Group, National Welfare Benefits Handbook, 26th edn: 1996/97

In 1992, there were 13.6 million people living on or below the income support level. That is 24 per cent of the population. Some 4.7 million people, eight per cent of the population, are living below even Income Support level. This includes 830,000 children.[58] The real situation facing many people is typified by this young mother:

> 'I'd say in a good week we'd have about £30 for food, in a very good week. In a bad week we'd have £20 – and that's for the four of us. On a particularly tough fortnight we would eat one meal a day so that the kids could eat, because they don't understand the fact that food costs money, and if you haven't got the money you can't buy the food.'
> Mother of two, summer 1996

Downsizing diet: a necessary evil

The abolition of safety nets which took decades to weave has wrought devastation among Britain's most vulnerable communities. It has combined with the shrinking of British industry and the loss of jobs. Families subjected to the pressures of declining incomes, job insecurity and debt, are forced to make drastic cuts in their living standards. Food is the largest single item of household expenditure; it's also the most flexible. It has to bear the brunt of enforced domestic savings. Diet is in the firing line. Nutritional adequacy falters and fails. As poverty becomes more severely entrenched than ever before, diet is downsized – and with it, health. What's worse, people know the harm that will come to them. A woman described the effects of moving off decent wages onto benefit:

> 'I've always worked, so being on benefit was something new to me. It's something of a nightmare. All the time you are looking for the cheapest of brands. My diet has changed dramatically. Basically now I'm eating shite. I've put on three stone.'

Official food consumption statistics show that:
- people in the largest poor families eat, on average, the equivalent of less than a couple of sprouts per person per day for their vegetables
- the fresh fruit consumption of the largest poor families is the equivalent of only one quarter of an apple per person per day
- in the best-off families the amount of fruit consumed per person rises as the family grows larger. In poor families the reverse is true: the more children there are the less fruit each one eats

- some large poor families now eat twice as much sugar as they do fresh green vegetables, and more fat than fresh fruit (measured by weight)
- in recent years the amount of fresh green vegetables eaten by the poor has dropped considerably. In larger poor families, it is now only one third of the amount eaten in 1980.[59]

As we come to the end of the century we are also at the nadir of official concern or action about poor diet. The last decade and a half has seen the systematic reduction in state support for the diets of the most vulnerable. The nutritional protection for children in particular has been undermined – even at a time when the likelihood of their living in poverty has climbed alarmingly to almost one in three. There is evidence that poor children were more dependent on school meals than their better-off peers. Research published in 1983 showed that lower income children received a greater percentage of their daily intake of many essential nutrients from school meals than did upper income children: particularly protein, calcium, iron, vitamin C and fibre. 'The fact that lower income children were receiving larger school meals and a significantly higher proportion of a day's nutrient intake from school meals further suggests that the school dinners were relied on more heavily in the lower income group. Clearly, school dinners fulfilled a more important nutritional role for children from the lower income homes than for children from the more affluent homes.'[60]

Unpicking the nutritional safety net

1971 Education (Milk) Act, with minor exceptions, abolished free school milk to children older than seven.

1980 Education Act. School meals deregulated: the national fixed price, minimum nutritional standards and the statutory duty on LEAs to provide school meals for all was abolished.

1986 Social Security Act. Number of children entitled to free school meals cut by one third: 400,000 children of very low wage families had their entitlement to free school meals taken away. Made the provision of milk in schools discretionary not obligatory, prohibited local authorities from using state funds to provide school milk and made it illegal to provide milk free for the children of low wage parents.

1988 Special dietary additions – payments made over and above general benefit levels to meet medically prescribed diets – abolished.

1988 Local Government Act introduced compulsory competitive tendering, obliging LEAs to put school meals out to tender.

1988 The replacement of the single-payment grant scheme for items such as cookers and fridges with Social Fund loans.

1992 Further social security changes meant that the children of 35,000 families had their rights to free school meals withdrawn.

1992 All secondary school children lost their entitlement to receive education in nutrition and cooking skills under the National Curriculum.

1995 November budget: the Government opted out of the EU scheme which subsidises the use of milk as an ingredient in school meals and which subsidises the provision of milk to drink in secondary schools.

There was far more focused concern from government about the diets of the poor in the Victorian era than there has been in our time. Instead, inadequate benefits, low wages and the food insecurity that accompanies them have been used as a spur to drive people into poorly paid jobs.

Defining modern malnutrition

'There's poverty that you'd never believe. I've had children coming in here with no food. Half this estate worries about where the next meal is coming from.'
Retired dinner lady

'Two days before pay day, you see people walking around the estate knocking on friends' doors, asking if they've got a tin of beans or some Weetabix they can give the kids.'
Mother of two children

'There is real poverty. I don't think the government realizes. When the kids haven't been fed it isn't mismanagement. It's just not having enough money.'
Grandmother

Manifestly, food poverty exists in Britain. It's not the starvation found currently in many developing countries. It doesn't correspond to the problems caused by unequal distribution, described in the 1930s. But there is a problem of less than optimal nutrition:

'I don't always eat. I sometimes have breakfast (about four days a week). I always go without lunch (just a cup of tea) and very often without an evening meal. I might eat up what the kids leave. Saturday evening is the only good meal of the week.'
Mother of two children, husband on a low wage

Cost per hundred calories

Food	Cost (£)
Custard cream biscuits	0.02
White sliced bread	0.03
Wholemeal rolls	0.04
Frozen chips	0.04
Boiled potatoes	0.07
Carrots	0.20
Broccoli	0.74
Lettuce	0.76
Tomatoes	0.80
Celery	1.03

Food	Cost (£)
Pork sausages	0.10
Meat pie	0.11
Lean pork	0.33
Fish fingers	0.13
Frozen cod fillet	0.95
Chocolate bar	0.08
Corn snacks	0.12
Apples	0.19
Oranges	0.30
Full fat milk	0.07
Skimmed milk	0.13

Source: Food Commission, 1993

Although there must be very few people who simply cannot access sufficient calories, the requirement to fill up is the overriding priority for many low-income consumers:

> *'Everyone on benefit wants to feed their children better, but you tend to think of them having enough food so they're not hungry rather than good quality food and be feeling a bit hungry between meals.'*
> Mother of two living on benefit

Faced with this dilemma it is rational to shop for cheap, filling food, and many people decide to forgo such food items as fresh fruit and many fresh vegetables altogether. It's a lot cheaper to get your calories from custard creams than from celery – as the above chart shows. People regularly go without main meals, often for days at a time, particularly before the fortnightly giro. As one single parent said:

> *'By Monday and Tuesday it's quite bad - I might go for two days without a main meal - I just eat, like, a sandwich at lunchtime and perhaps one at supper if we had enough bread. I was standing in the Post Office once, in the queue, and I came over feeling quite awful and I had to sit down, I felt*

embarrassed and I got up and then I fainted. It was a Thursday. I wouldn't have had a main meal on the Tuesday or the Wednesday.'

These are the faces of modern malnutrition. Yet there is still profound resistance to the concept of food poverty at official level. Both the National Food Alliance and the Nutrition Task Force's Low Income Project Team have been prevented from using the term 'food poverty' by civil servants anxious to keep ministers sweet. By the same token, health inequalities are reduced to health 'variations'.

How to define food poverty

Food poverty can be variously defined. Sometimes it's simply by reference to affordability: 'the inability to afford an adequate healthy diet.' Other people stress access to food. An American definition runs: 'the condition in which the level of nutrition necessary for good health is not being met because of a lack of access to food.'

I believe that a much better definition is the one derived from a study of low-income women in upstate New York:

> *'the inability to acquire or consume an adequate quality or sufficient quantity of food in socially acceptable ways, or the uncertainty that one will be able to do so.'* [61]

An affordability definition conventionally invokes issues about price, income and sensible spending. An access definition is wider and includes geographic, social, practical and cultural issues, like whether people can get to the shops. Adding a 'social acceptability' rider incorporates the idea of social norms and social inclusion – it's not acceptable that people should eat pet food, for example. Some observers may take exception to the rider 'or the uncertainty that one will be able to do so'. But this does reflect the experience of many people struggling to feed themselves and their families, for whom the anxiety and uncertainty are as bad as the hunger. 'We had sleepless nights wondering how we were going to eat,' said the parents of two children, caught in the poverty trap, who had moved from benefits to low-wage employment.

Casting a shadow on the future

Whatever definition you adopt, it is important to acknowledge that food poverty is linked to a wider range of causes other than income inadequacy and has specific consequences which cannot be ignored. Poor nutrition doesn't just affect today's generation. Peggy and Arthur Wynn, in their 1993 Caroline Walker lecture 'No Nation Can Rise Above the Level of its Women', and through their lifetime of study and campaigning devoted to the importance of nutrition, have sketched the long shadow that poor nutrition casts down the generations. Inadequate diet is capable of producing handicaps across generations. These impairments can persist throughout life. 'Direct and adverse consequences can affect a child's health, education and future employability, and there are demonstrable costs to society in each instance.'[62] Mild malnutrition is an important independent cause of cognitive defects.[63] Even nutritional deficiencies of a relatively short-term nature influence children's behaviour, ability to concentrate, and to perform complex tasks.[64]

The nutritional consequences of neglecting nutrition are beginning to show their effects. A nutrition gap is opening up between rich and poor, and

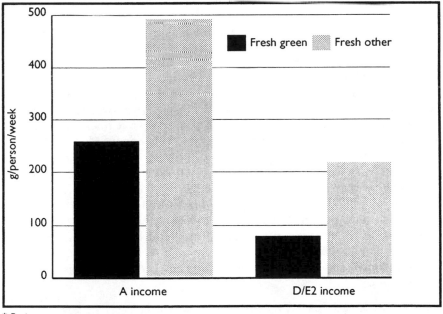

Fresh vegetable consumption in families with 3 children*

* By income group
Source MAFF, National Food Survey 1994, HMSO, 1995

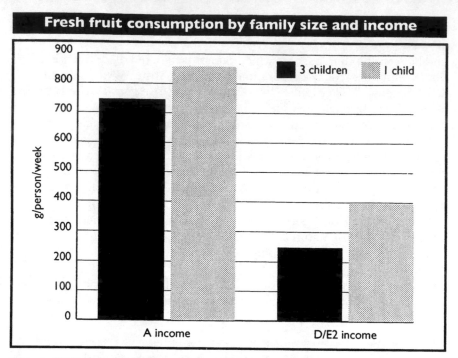

Fresh fruit consumption by family size and income

y-axis: g/person/week

Legend: ■ 3 children ▦ 1 child

x-axis: A income, D/E2 income

Source: MAFF, *National Food Survey 1994*, HMSO, London, 1995

families with children are showing alarmingly low levels of consumption of certain foods – usually healthy foods.

The widening food gap – and its health effects

In some notable respects the food gap between rich and poor has widened in recent years. The gap in fruit consumption, shown above, demonstrates that the fruit consumption of the poor is declining while that of the better-off is increasing fast – thereby reversing a decades-long trend towards more equal consumption. Given what we know about the protective properties of fresh fruit consumption, it is worrying that average consumption is actually declining amongst low-income groups. Recent research found that daily consumption of fresh fruit was associated with a 24 per cent reduction in mortality from ischaemic heart disease, a 32 per cent reduction in mortality from cerebrovascular disease, and a 21 per cent reduction in all cause mortality when compared with less frequent fruit consumption.[65] Trends towards a food gap can also be seen for fat consumption.

Sources for both fruit and fat graphs: Nelson, M *Social-class trends in British diet, 1860-1980* in *Food, Diet and Economic Change Past and Present.* Edited by Catherine Geissler and Derek J Oddy, Leicester University Press, 1993.
With update from MAFF *National Food Survey 1994*, HMSO, London, 1995

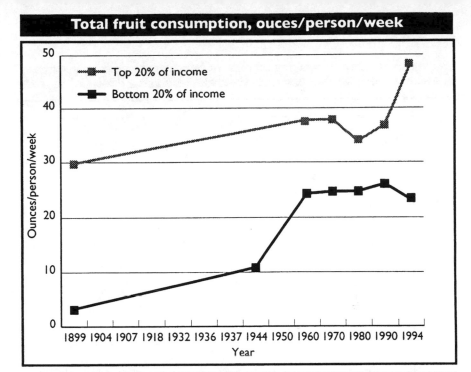

Total fruit consumption, ouces/person/week

- Top 20% of income
- Bottom 20% of income

Ounces/person/week

Year

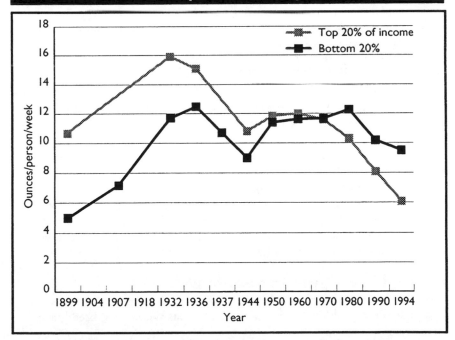

Total fat consumption, ounces/person/week

- Top 20% of income
- Bottom 20%

Ounces/person/week

Year

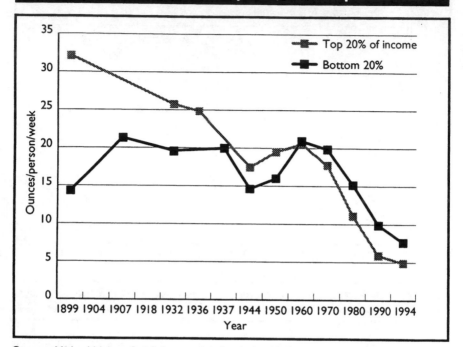

Sugar and preserves consumption, ounces/person/week

Top 20% of income
Bottom 20%

Ounces/person/week

1899 1904 1907 1918 1932 1936 1937 1944 1950 1960 1970 1980 1990 1994
Year

Source: Michael Nelson *Social-class trends in British diet, 1860-1980* in *Food, Diet and Economic Change Past and Present.* Edited by Catherine Geissler and Derek J Oddy, Leicester University Press, 1993. With update from MAFF *National Food Survey 1994*, HMSO, London, 1995.

The gap for sugar is less marked, but nevertheless shows that the poor consume more sugar: it is an important source of cheap calories.

The poorest twenty per cent of families with children spend, on average, only £12.82 per person each week on food.[66] Many spend far less. Among poor lone parent families, average weekly food spending is only £11.51 a head. I have interviewed many families where the food money is only £5 per person per week. It's clear that low spending levels like this mean that cost is the main factor driving food purchases. What are the nutritional consequences both in terms of quality and quantity?

Poor diets will lead to poor health
'Coping within a limited food budget is often at the expense of foods known by householders to be 'healthier', such as wholemeal bread, lean

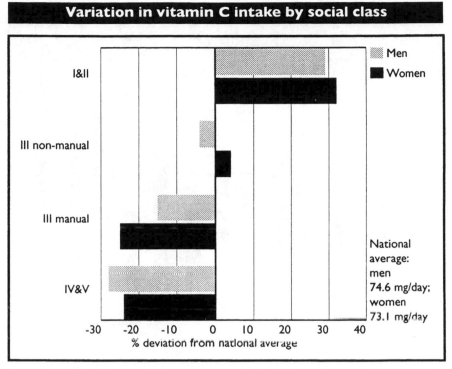

Variation in vitamin C intake by social class

Source: MAFF, The *Dietary and Nutritional Survey of British Adults - Further Analysis.* HMSO, 1990

meat, and fruit. Some respondents have reported that they regularly go without food because there is not enough money, or in order to meet the needs of other household members. Young householders, the unemployed, those on benefit or very low incomes, and especially those living in local authority accommodation with rent or fuel deductions from benefit payments, have the greatest difficulties and the worst diets.'[67]

Particularly large differences exist for antioxidant vitamins, due to the markedly lower consumption of fruit and vegetables by poorer people (see chart, above).[68] Analysis of the government Adult Nutrition Survey found that more than one in four women in households receiving benefits had diets deficient in iron, vitamin A, thiamin, riboflavin, vitamin B6 and vitamin C.[69] The extent of this nutritional inadequacy is well illustrated by Dowler and Calvert (see chart, over the page).

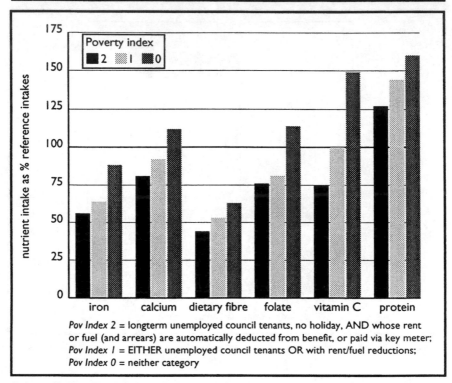

Pov Index 2 = longterm unemployed council tenants, no holiday, AND whose rent or fuel (and arrears) are automatically deducted from benefit, or paid via key meter;
Pov Index 1 = EITHER unemployed council tenants OR with rent/fuel reductions;
Pov Index 0 = neither category

Source: Dowler, E and Calvert, C *Nutrition and diet in lone-parent families in London*, Family Policy Studies Centre, London, 1995

In other words, people from lower socio-economic groups have lower micro-nutrient intakes because of the poorer quality of their food. The Scottish Heart Study found that the nutrient density (the amount of a nutrient per 1000 calories) of foods eaten by poorer people was 20 to 25 per cent less than foods eaten by the better-off.[70] Even when intakes may not be technically 'deficient' according to Department of Health recommendations, they may still be inadequate. There is growing evidence for the protective effect of anti-oxidant vitamins and minerals against chronic diseases such as cancer and coronary heart disease at levels above the recommended intakes. This suggests that the low intakes of poor people, often combined with a higher environmental requirement, due to higher rates of infection and smoking, may directly increase their risk of heart disease and common cancers and amounts to a new form of malnutrition – a form with devastating potential for public health.

Feelings are as important as nutrients

In the last few years there has been some acknowledgement of the problem of the links between income inequality and health. We have become used to the material explanations of health inequalities – factors such as getting enough good food. Certainly nutrition plays an important role in the development of many diseases. And there is certainly an income-related gradient in the major causes of death and illness. The effect of this gradient is remarkable. People in the least privileged circumstances are likely to die about eight years earlier than those who are more affluent.[71] The total excess deaths in the more disadvantaged half of the population is equivalent to a major air crash or shipwreck every day.[72]

The reasons for this excess death and illness among the disadvantaged are complex, and nutritional inadequacy is an important contributory factor. But is it simply that poverty affects food consumption and leads to lower levels of certain nutrients? Is it solely a matter of the intake of particular nutrients? There is important new evidence to suggest this is not so.

The findings of Richard Wilkinson in particular have drawn attention to the lethal effects of social divisions themselves.[73] He notes that death rates from the main causes, including infections, cardiovascular diseases and cancers are highest in countries where income inequality is greatest; where the gap between the rich and poor is at its widest. This can also be seen within countries, such as in different states in the US. States with the smallest income inequalities also have the lowest death rates.

Part of the excess mortality and morbidity in those states or countries with the greatest inequality may be explained statistically: there is a higher proportion of low-income families, with higher rates of death and disease. However, it seems there is something about inequality itself which causes people to suffer and die. Social divisions are now being recognized as harmful in themselves. In addition to the direct physical effects of poverty, Wilkinson stresses the importance of psychological consequences 'in terms of stress, self esteem, and social relations.'[74]

Quite apart from the nutritional consequences of food poverty, there are considerable social and psychological stresses involved. To be food poor is to be highly stressed. Women seem to absorb most of the stress of food poverty, which may partly account for the higher levels of smoking amongst the poor, particularly lone parents.[75] Perhaps the saddest thing is the feelings parents have towards their children. One mother described her shock at her children's acceptance of what they couldn't have. 'What really amazes me is how much they accept going without.' Another mother said simply: 'Sometimes when my son has said to me he's hungry, I just feel very desperate and alone, and a bit of a failure I suppose.'

When providers can't provide

It is not difficult to see how the emotional stress that poverty engenders, particularly among parents, may lead to poor health and eventual early death. Food is, after all, the medium through which the first emotional attachment between mother and child is expressed and secured. Our feelings around food are clearly capable of engendering profoundly powerful messages to us about our relationship with ourselves and others we love. It is an important key to self-esteem. So when someone is robbed of the means to provide food for themselves and others in the way they want, it is not just their immediate physical health which is damaged but their general sense of competence and autonomy. The feelings of hopelessness may, in a vicious circle, lead to other health-damaging behaviour, such as smoking. It is no coincidence, I believe, that levels of smoking are so much higher amongst Britain's poor, and particularly among lone parents, than among the better-off. But food poverty also leads to another behaviour associated with deprivation – crime.

Food poverty causes crime

The social stresses of food poverty are even such that there is now food poverty-related crime. We hear much about the increase in crime and rather less about the causes. But it is a fact that some crime is being committed so that people can eat.

> 'Let's face it, we'd all steal to feed our children.'
> Mother of three children

> 'I don't know anyone who eats anything like a decent diet who isn't working illegally or going into debt to help them fund it.'
> Family Centre Manager

> 'It's sad when they've got to steal to eat.'
> Grandmother

'People are committing burglary now for food rather than taking the TV or video to sell.'
Father of two children

'Students are prostituting themselves to eat. They are actually going on the streets so they can eat and pay the rent. A friend of mine went with one and he asked her why she did it, and she said it was so she could eat.'
Father of one child

Food poverty related crime is also being committed by shops which hold benefit books. The benefit book is in effect held as security on the food debts which the holder of the book has incurred at that shop – usually a very expensive local shop. The extent of this practice is unknown; people are very reluctant to expose it. But the practice is not uncommon.

'Poverty is when you draw your dole money and it belongs to the man in the grocery shop, so they have to shop there, and it is a very expensive shop. He lets them run up a bill, provided they leave their books there. And he lets them go on and on.'
Woman in her fifties

A polarized food economy

'Drugs are readily available around here. In fact it's easier to buy drugs than fresh fruit and vegetables – and there is more selection.'
Resident of a deprived housing estate

We have seen that inadequate income has a deleterious impact on diet, and that inequality is also harmful through its psychosocial impact. But there is another, more material mechanism by which the gap between richest and poorest increases the effects of poor nutrition and stress: through food retailing.

The growth in income inequality has exerted pressure on the distribution of food retailing provision. Food retailing has followed national income trends in becoming more unequal. This is hardly surprising: in 1979 the top twenty per cent of earners accounted for 35% of total household spending. By 1995 it had grown to 49%. The share of spending by the bottom forty per cent of earners halved in the same period from 24.5% to

12.5%.[76] The amounts spent on food by rich and poor differ enormously now. The top ten per cent of households spend upwards of £119 a week on food and drink, whilst the bottom ten per cent spend only £25 a week.[77] The top ten per cent spend more on food alone than the bottom ten per cent's total income for all their needs.

Out-of-town suits the well-off

It was partly this deepening income divide which lay behind the explosive growth in supermarkets sited away from city centres. The better-off, with their cars, large bank balances, and plenty of food storage space, wanted to maximize their convenience with one-stop shopping. The supermarkets got cheap greenfield sites which suited their distribution networks, straight in off the motorway. But the move to out-of-town meant that shops were on average further from home. The distance consumers travelled for shopping increased by 60 per cent between the mid 1970s and the end of the 1980s.[78] But 31 per cent of British households are without a car (84 per cent in the poorest tenth). For anyone that is without a car, for the inner city resident, for people living on a peripheral housing estate, or for the rural poor – in short, for people outside the well-off mainstream, these high street clearances were the food equivalent of disconnecting the water supply.

The contradictions in modern food retailing are extraordinary. While the major retailers like Tesco and Sainsbury's are busy 'micro-marketing', minutely targeting their products at the niche markets they have identified via their loyalty cards, great swathes of our fellow citizens have been ignored by the major retailers. Some of the worst ravages of food poverty occur in the sink housing estates used by local authorities and housing associations for temporary accommodation for 'priority need' families. The term implies they are given some kind of extra help. In fact these policies of social dumping – putting everyone on pitifully low incomes together – merely has the effect of concentrating poverty. Incarceration on these housing estates is a sort of internal exile. Exile from the rest of society, exile from the kind of facilities, including food shops, which the rest of the population take for granted.

> *'It costs money to get to the shops. It costs us £7 to get to the shops and back – and we are only spending £30 a week on food for all four of us.'*
> Woman living with her husband and two children

One of the reasons why the poor have a particularly hard time affording a healthy diet is that they have to pay more for their food than the better-off.

> 'I get the bus into town because I like to go to Tesco's, it's cheaper. But the only problem with that is that I can't get as much as I'd like because I have to carry it home. I can only afford to go in once a week, so for everything else that I can't manage to carry home I have to buy from Spar, which is dearer.'
> Resident of Barne Barton, Plymouth

> 'We used to have two or three supermarkets in the square. Now there is only one – and it can charge what it likes.'
> Resident of Barne Barton, Plymouth

Our current food economy actually penalizes the poor by charging them higher prices than the better-off. Food costs more in poorer areas than it does in richer ones. This is sometimes called the 'consumer detriment'. [79] Several studies have compared prices in different areas and found poorer areas to be more expensive than richer ones, especially for healthier foods.[80] A recent study carried out at the London School of Economics comparing different prices for a similar basket of goods at different shops found that prices in small shops (corner shops, village shops, convenience stores, independent small supermarkets) were on average just over 23 per cent higher than big shops (large supermarket chains and discounters). Depending on the types of food bought, the price difference between shopping in small or in big shops could amount to between 10 and 30 per cent of the total income of some pensioner couples.[81]

Deliberately excluding the poor

Sometimes the poor are deliberately excluded from access to the very cheapest forms of retailing. The really cheap stores – the out-of-town shed shops, so called warehouse clubs, such as Costco, offer astonishing bargains. But they specifically exclude the poor. The success of its 210 warehouse clubs in the US has apparently convinced the company it doesn't need low-spending, small-scale shoppers from society's poorer grades clogging up the aisles.[82] According to Clive Vaughan of retail research company Verdict Research: 'Individuals are allowed to join provided they have an above average income and stable employment. They're going for doctors and solicitors with Volvos and big houses to store things in. They are going for *Which?*-reading ABs looking for bargains. Lower social groups are catered for by discount supermarkets such as Kwik Save and Netto'.[83]

It's an easy assumption, often casually made, that everyone is better-off because of the developments we have seen in modern food retailing. But to whom has the British model of food capitalism been of benefit? Is it really to everyone? To customers as well as shareholders? To poor as well as rich consumers? There must be very few people who as food consumers would actually choose old soviet-style food and agriculture policies over the 'cathedrals of choice' which is the Western model of food retailing.[84] And yet, and yet ... go to Britain's deprived areas and you will meet people whose lives more closely mirror those in old communist cultures than the pride of the West. Food poverty demonstrates, in our own country, the foolishness of separating the market from the humanity which it is supposed to serve .

Food has a social dimension

So I am not arguing for the replacement of the food capitalism we have in favour of old soviet-style central planning. I am arguing that we should recognize how the market has worked in recent times. Its economic dynamism takes it where the profits are greatest; it chases the purses of the average and better-off. This is not surprising: its duties are to maximize profits for shareholders, not to replace the crumbling welfare state. But we have to keep in mind the need for social cohesion in food. Our own history has some very pertinent lessons. Perhaps one of the reasons why deaths dropped so dramatically in the period of narrowing income differentials between 1940 and 1951, was not just that rationing ensured that nutrients were divided more equally through society, but that the social cohesiveness that was around at that time, of which common rations were but a symbol, was powerfully protective of health. Everyone felt they were 'in it together', and having the same food rights served to obliterate social distinctions. Today food has become once again a symbol of differences, of social as well as nutritional distinction and division: I can afford to keep healthy with my 'five portions of fruit and vegetables a day', but you cannot.

What can be done

> 'What we can eat depends on what we are able to acquire. The mere presence of food in the economy, or in the market, does not entitle a person to consume it.'[85]
> Dreze and Sen, *Hunger and Public Action*

Taken as a whole, Britain has enough food for its needs. We have aggregate food security. We grow and produce our own food in abundance and import what we cannot meet ourselves. But it is not enough.

Food poverty in the UK is a distribution problem, not a problem of production. Not distribution in the sense of efficient road networks, but in the sense of fairness – what has been called distributive justice.[86] Access to an adequate healthy diet should be an entitlement. Prolonged high rates of unemployment, growing income inequality, and the declining value of real wages and welfare benefits have all systematically eroded the capability of individuals and communities to secure food. We cannot fight modern malnutrition unless and until we recognise that the right to enough good food is a basic human right; and until Britain adopts policies which address inequality of income and problems of access.

Government failures and inaction

At the moment access to a healthy diet depends on well-paid employment, or other adequate income, and living in the right area. In other words, it is not an entitlement. And yet the UK is a signatory to the International Covenant on Economic, Social and Cultural Rights (1966), to the UN Convention on the Rights of the Child, as well as to the EU council recommendation that 'least favoured citizens' have guarantee of sufficient, stable and reliable resources and benefits.

This year, 1996, is the UN Year for the Elimination of Poverty. In November 1996, Rome hosts the World Food Summit. In each forum, Britain will seek to portray itself as an advanced industrial country where everyone has food security. It will be a sham. The UK will attempt to demonstrate a commitment to upholding basic human rights – while at the same time pursuing policies which continue to undermine them. The attack on the welfare state continues. The UK rejects the idea of social and economic rights and stands alone against the EU Social Chapter. The closure of food shops is allowed to continue. And what real policy options are being considered? Community self-help, charity and the free market.

One government initiative: gagged

The sole governmental initiative in food poverty was the setting up of the Nutrition Task Force Low Income Project Team (LIPT) which was charged with 'collating and disseminating examples of good local practice which might enable those on a low income to ensure they eat a healthy diet.'[87] The LIPT report was the first post-war official recognition of the modern food poverty problem. It made a number of recommendations in April 1996. The *Observer* welcomed it as 'a blue-print for mass national action which would be the biggest healthy eating drive since the "Dig for Victory" campaign of the Second World War.'[88] Yet LIPT was prevented from discussing any income issues; benefits were ruled off the agenda. Even after LIPT's truncated analysis was published, the government merely noted LIPT's recommendations. The Inter-Departmental Group on Public Health are merely earmarking a small amount for research on evaluation of projects.

A network of initiatives

By far and away the most energetic action on tackling food poverty has come from within deprived communities themselves, principally by setting up projects to try to improve the access of residents of deprived areas to healthier food items. There are now well over 140 food projects across England and Wales, and many more in Scotland, which have been brought together under the National Food Alliance's National Food Poverty Network. In keeping with the spirit of the age, this network is not funded by government, but owes its existence to the National Lottery.

There has even been an initiative by the retailers. The Institute of Grocery Distribution started a scheme called *Provision* in 1993 to channel potentially wasted food to charities, mostly to those caring for the homeless. *Provision's* current turnover is £2.7 million a year.[89]

There have also of course been the market responses by food retailers to the changes in income distribution. Whilst the major retailers have moved up-market chasing the purses of the average and better-off, the discounters have come in to cater for the poor. The food market is becoming more polarized, both in terms of quality and spatially, as producers and retailers target rich and poor as separate markets.

Not surprisingly, given the growth in the numbers of poor consumers, the discounters are doing very well: in 1995 Aldi, Netto and Lidl increased their combined UK sales by more than 50 per cent to £1.2 billion.[90] Discounters are attractive to poorer consumers because of the range of 'value' products and the fact that they site in poorer areas. But there is a sting in the tale of their success. Discounters often don't stock fresh food, and they have in turn encouraged the major retailers to stock a bigger range of value products – so that now, the cheapest prices are not necessarily found at discounters (see table, over the page).

The uncertainty of worthy projects

But will charity schemes, the free market or underfunded community projects be enough to solve the problem? Community food projects appear to be making an important contribution to tackling the problems of food poverty but they are very insecurely funded, extremely limited and dependent upon volunteers to survive. We do not yet know whether they are effectively targeted. The LIPT felt that the scale of the impact of low income on diet-related health meant that locally-based projects, worthy as they are, cannot meet the food needs of the majority of low-income communities.[91]

Community responses have been impressive, but they contain troubling dilemmas and contradictions.[92] Some see community solutions as forcing the underclass to be responsible for its own succour. Others see the retreat to community for solutions as a dangerous abdication of responsibility by the politicians. Again, consider the analogy of water supply: would it be acceptable for households to have to rely on volunteers bringing water from stand pipes because a whole community had an inadequate water supply? Or would we demand to see a more constructive solution? Others see the community development approach as the only realistic option for communities upon whom the contented majority has turned its back.

It is easy to see the appeal of the community development approach for the present administration: it smacks of the self-help ethos, involves

Prices of common products: discounters aren't always lowest

Product	Pack size	Aldi	Asda	Kwik Save	Lidl
Baked beans	420g	0.09	0.09	0.09	0.09
Tomato soup	400g	0.23	0.21	0.19	0.19
Corned beef	340g	0.59	0.59	0.59	0.53
Corn flakes	500g	0.45	0.49	0.45	0.39
Medium sliced white loaf	800g	0.25	0.27	0.25	0.25
Coffee granules	100g	0.79	0.79	0.79	0.79
Tea bags	80	0.69	0.35	0.35	0.89
Butter	250g	0.59	0.59	0.59	0.59
Fish fingers	10	0.45	0.35	0.35	0.53
Washing-up liquid	1 litre	0.12	0.21	0.11	0.12
Washing powder	E10	2.99	2.45	2.44	2.99
Toilet rolls	4-pack	0.59	0.66	0.97	0.59
Frozen chicken portions	price/kg	1.53	1.40	1.52	1.53
Fruit scones	10	0.65	0.49	0.48	0.49
Mushrooms	price/kg	2.48	2.18	1.68	2.42
Sausages	1lb(454g)	0.79	0.47	0.38	0.59
Vanilla ice cream	2 litre	0.79	0.79	0.77	0.55
Long grain rice	1kg	0.79	0.78	0.78	0.79
Rice pudding	396g	0.25	0.25	0.27	0.25
ADJUSTED BASKET TOTAL* (£)		15.11	13.41	13.04	14.57
Total less chicken & mushrooms (£)		11.10	9.83	9.84	10.62

* Some prices adjusted to conform to most common pack size
Source: Verdict Research/Super Marketing, July 1996

vanishingly small resources and can be encouraged without at the same time having to admit to the existence of poverty. Ironically, parts of the conventional market are already attempting to undermine the activities of community groups, with wholesalers often refusing to sell to community food-buying co-operatives because of their other customers – small local shops who fear competition from community projects.

A sense of belonging
Time will tell what the lasting impact of food projects will be. Certainly they are trying to address the key issues of access and affordability. It may be that their greater contribution to reducing the effects of food poverty is in ameliorating the psychological effects: the stress, feelings of isolation

Morrisons	Netto	Safeway	Sainsbury	Somerfield	Tesco	Av price (£)
0.16	0.09	0.09	0.09	0.09	0.09	0.10
0.21	0.22	0.23	0.23	0.23	na	0.22
0.65	0.59	0.69	na	0.75	0.69	0.63
0.49	0.49	0.55	na	0.55	0.49	0.48
0.27	0.25	0.27	0.27	0.27	0.27	0.26
na	0.79	na	0.79	na	1.14	0.84
na	0.69	0.35	0.35	0.35	0.35	0.49
0.64	0.64	na	0.59	na	0.59	0.60
0.39	0.33	0.39	0.39	na	0.39	0.40
0.21	0.11	0.21	0.21	0.21	0.11	0.16
na	1.99	na	2.45	2.54	2.54	2.55
0.59	0.59	0.75	0.75	0.75	0.75	0.70
1.78	2.89	1.97	1.28	1.92	1.42	1.72
0.49	0.58	0.49	0.49	na	na	0.52
1.96	2.37	2.62	2.17	3.50	2.25	2.36
0.65	0.59	0.47	0.55	0.54	0.47	0.55
0.79	0.69	0.78	0.78	0.79	0.78	0.75
na	0.79	na	0.84	0.84	0.84	0.81
0.25	0.35	0.25	0.25	0.29	0.25	0.27
13.86	15.04	14.55	13.59	15.98	14.16	14.40
10.12	9.78	9.96	10.14	10.56	10.49	10.31

and general hopelessness. Through do-it-yourself, bartering, voluntary work, sharing and subsistence agriculture, they offer the autonomy and independence so effectively stifled by the money economy. While richer people can buy autonomy, community projects offer it to the poor, and go some way to release them from subordination to the cash economy.

My own feeling is that community action is important but that, to be effective, it must be supported by adequate resources and a measure of real power in the local food economy (eg over shop siting decisions). If not, community development food projects will go in much the same way as community mental health care policy: a good idea, driven to fail by government adopting it as a cheap solution. It needs money to work.

Charities are not the whole answer

Is charity the answer? It is of course scandalous that we have developed food systems which produce vast quantities of unwanted food whilst at the same time there are people dependent on hand-outs. Perhaps soup kitchens are both necessary and successful for the destitute. But there is an old Russian saying 'Free cheese only comes in mousetraps.' Charity undoubtedly gives large food industrialists the chance to look like good corporate citizens. But food industry charity must only be acceptable if at the same time industry is recognising its own contribution to the current situation and working to change that.

There are real long-term problems with going down the charity road. Do we really want to develop dependence on the private charity of the food industry? There are plenty of examples of food banks – in the USA 21.8 million people are dependent on emergency food aid, and in Canada, it's 2.8 million people. Intended as emergency relief, these schemes become entrenched. The food retailers do not even bother putting food on shop shelves, they donate it directly to food banks in return for tax breaks. Toronto now has more food banks than McDonalds outlets.[93] Wouldn't the food industry here rather have consumers who have enough money to be able to buy their products? Are soup kitchens really the answer for poor families; do we want to see queues of our poor children standing in line after school for an evening meal?

Will the free market, with its 'No Frills' and 'Value' product lines be the answer? They certainly help, very much. But they do not of themselves address the problem of access to food shops, and the value lines tend not to apply to fresh, low fat, high fibre foods, like fresh fruit and vegetables. I do not think Caroline Walker would be very impressed with them today! In any case a chilling appraisal of the prospects for low priced lines appeared in an article in *SuperMarketing*:

> 'The City at present remains unconvinced that the major multiples need to put too much emphasis on their value lines, even though for some sectors of the community pricing is of vital importance.'[94]

Off-loading responsibility for the core problem

The problem with all these 'solutions' is that none of them really addresses the core problems. And all of them smack of the government off-loading its welfare responsibilities. Charities and deprived communities alone cannot defend food security. Our social welfare system was meant to prevent poverty. It fails not because welfare does not work, but because benefits do not spell out an entitlement to food security either in terms of legal rights (which they never have), nor nowadays in terms of adequate money for food (which we once had).

Most people want to escape from food poverty through secure long-term, adequately paid employment. They do not want to stay in the benefit 'system'. Any measures which help them to enter employment of that kind are therefore important. It is also necessary to adapt the social security system to the flexible labour market so that people do not have to gamble their own or their children's dietary health by entering insecure employment. But even with measures to help people back to work, there will still be households who through no fault of their own are dependent on benefits. There should always be a guaranteed minimum income which covers all basic needs including adequate food.

Looking after the children

We must also re-establish a nutritional safety-net especially for children. This should be done by re-instating old entitlements, such as the provision of free school meals at a minimum nutritional standard, and imaginatively creating new ones.

Maud Pember Reeves wrote in 1913 that 'There should be no such thing as an underfed school child: an underfed child is a disgrace and a danger to the state.' They still are. A recent study comparing heights, weights and head circumference of primary school children found evidence of chronic undernutrition amongst those children from a deprived area. The deprived five year olds were on average 2.25cm shorter than their better-off peers.[95]

We also urgently need to provide nutritional support to children before they reach school. A recent study of children aged 18-30 months concluded 'The main finding of this study suggests that children living in poverty, in a post-industrial society, are still showing delayed growth due to under-nutrition which may have important long-term implications for health.'[96] The cost of the ill health must be considerable. A body of evidence suggests that early intervention is not only necessary, but can lead to impressive cost savings. The Women, Infants and Children (WIC) Food Supplement Program in the USA, which helps to ensure that women with low incomes have an adequate diet during pregnancy, found that for every dollar spent, medical costs saved during the first 60 days after birth were between $2.84 and $3.90, for the newborns alone. We need a WIC programme in the UK. And how to pay for all this? Why not use unclaimed benefit? Up to £3.2 billion was unclaimed in 1993.[97] It would only be using money which was intended for the poor anyway.

Retailers' responsibilities

Ensuring food security is not just about state action and adequate income. Particular regions and neighbourhoods are marginalised by economic forces, which are increasingly global. Local communities are robbed of control over their food economy as retailers decide where to site (elsewhere) and what to stock entirely according to the profit motive. Can food retailing have a purpose other than the ruthless pursuit of profit? Can it recognize its own interest in adopting a wider responsibility? It is embedded in the society in which it operates. And as such it must be capable of justifying and legitimizing itself to every section of that society.

If food retailing is to be more responsive to deprived communities, it will need to invest money. It calls for a new commitment from the food industry and some creative policies from government. The food industry must grasp the nettle of serving and supplying the whole of our complex modern society. And serving it in partnership: not by giving parcels of charitable aid, but by comprehensive fair trade. The present system cannot continue. It's a system which allows major retailers to dump the costs of their responsibilities onto the most vulnerable, by abandoning their poorest customers in the pursuit of the better-off.

A different type of food economy

I am suggesting a different model of the food economy, not one which forgets profits, but one which also has the goals of sustainability, social justice and community regeneration. This will require a more activist approach to the management of the food economy. Laissez-faire policies have given us swathes of food retailing deserts, an annual food trade deficit of £6.3 billion, and groups such as employees, the suppliers, (farmers and growers), and local communities are excluded from decision rights.[98] We need a more inclusive food economy than that. In the language of today, we need a stakeholder food economy. Tony Blair defines a stakeholder economy as one in which 'economic opportunity is widely dispersed and in which no group or class is excluded.'[99] In that economy we recognise that it's not just share-holders who have a legitimate interest in the food business, but employees, suppliers, consumers and communities. We will have power-sharing arrangements, so that supermarkets cannot just pull out of areas at the drop of a hat, but will serve needs which have been identified by and agreed with the community. We will recognise that as Joan Bavaria says 'there are two bottom lines, the financial and the social, and these need to be balanced.'[100]

As things stand, food retailing can come closer to the people or it can stay remote. It's up to the government, through financial incentives, to ensure that mainstream food retailing embraces the marginalised. And if it comes closer it will be in their interest. The discounters have proved, with their increased profit margins, that you can make money out of the poor. Perhaps William Temple was right when he said that 'The art of government in fact, is the art of so ordering life that self-interest prompts what justice demands.'

The ten commandments

1 The government and the country must recognise that food security is a basic human right, and that we express that right in a legal entitlement to an adequate food supply. This means guaranteeing an income adequate to meet basic needs, including food needs, and ensuring diversity of choice and easy access to local shopping facilities in deprived areas.

2 We must restore the system whereby benefits are uprated in line with average earnings rather than prices and ensure that benefits cover basic needs including the cost of a healthy diet.

3 Provide one-off grants, not loans, to allow people to buy essential equipment such as cookers and fridges.

4 Allow increased levels of earnings, child benefit, and a proportion of maintenance payment to be disregarded when calculating benefit levels.

5 Reinstate entitlement to Income Support for 16 and 17-year-olds.

6 Provide a safety net for children at nutritional risk by ensuring:
  ● provision of at least one nutritionally adequate meal every day in the term time and during school holidays
  ● The Nutrition Task Force's guidelines for school meals should be made statutory, not voluntary
  ● provision of school breakfast where appropriate to keep children from

being hungry
- reinstatement of free school milk in deprived areas
- provision of free school fruit in deprived areas
- provision of free school meals to children from families receiving Family Credit
- introduce WIC program to help prevent low birthweight babies.

7 Reinstate cooking, shopping and other food management skills as part of the National Curriculum at all ages.

8 For older people, increase eligibility for meals on wheels and introduce shopping carrying schemes to allow older people to remain in their homes and live independently.

9 Encourage the development of low cost food shopping through:
- providing street markets
- extending the range of 'value' lines in supermarkets and including fresh fruit and vegetables
- creating a map of 'shopping deserts' and areas of food insecurity and requiring local authorities and retailers to site new shops in these areas
- encouraging retailers to take more social responsibility in siting shops.

10 Local authorities should be required to support community food projects, and where possible to make up-and-coming technology (eg teleshopping, distance shopping) and delivery services available to low-income consumers. Local communities need to be given more power over local food and shopping policies.

Conclusion: we all need a solution to food poverty

> *'When there is a thorn in the foot the whole body must bend to pick it out otherwise it festers and the whole body is poisoned.'*
> African proverb

> *'We all live in the same society. It is a poorer society if it is diminished by unemployment, hopelessness and poverty. We all gain in security, in a sense of identity, and shared achievement from knowing that we all belong to one community. We will all lose in our quality of life if we each look out only for ourselves, but no one looks after the community.'*
> The late John Smith, MP

Our lives have in recent times been dominated by two main economic obsessions: cutting public expenditure and lowering the rate of income tax. These have been supported by a third desire; to reduce dependency on the state. These obsessions have permeated all aspects of social policy.

It turns out that the bracing disciplines of the market economy have not toughened us all up, or in some social-Darwinian way made the whole of society leaner and fitter. Instead, they have made our society ill. The market has built not a new utopia, but a new evil: that of a deeply divided nation. Sir Ian Gilmour, himself a Conservative, writes of the policies of the Thatcher era, 'Their polices were unrelentingly divisive and discriminatory against the poor, whose human dignity was relentlessly ignored.'[101] The reality of this attack on human dignity was brought home to me particularly vividly when I was researching this paper. I asked a woman in her 50s from a deprived inner city area to define what poverty meant now. 'Poverty' she said, 'is when girls have periods and they can't afford packets of STs.' It is to people in these financial straits that we are saying 'Go forth and buy broccoli.'

We are witnessing the emergence of a nutritional underclass. There is a group of Britons who are alienated from society, who cannot afford to shop in the same shops as the rest of us, who cannot buy the same food, people for whom going hungry is something they get used to, who every day are making choices between fulfilling one basic need or another. And a great many of the nutritionally disenfranchised are children. The recent developments in the food economy show us only what traditional Conservative thinkers have always known – that there are important areas of politics that cannot be left to the market without unacceptable social consequences. Hence there are areas in which government has to intervene for the good of society as a whole. I believe that the government should intervene now to protect the nation's diet.

But food has much more than a nutritional role. It is a means through which we express belonging. Throughout the Judaeo-Christian tradition, food has been the emblem of connection. The breaking of bread is the central part of worship and spiritual connection. Food deprivation harms more than our physical health.

A new generation has grown to adulthood under the shadow of endemic poverty. Our poor youngsters failed to gain from the booms of the 1980s and now they are being denied their fair share in the insecure 1990s. Their lives have been blunted by poverty. Their parents found themselves unable to provide the food they knew their children needed. They worked longer and longer hours, doubled up in jobs, took what they could to put food on the table. They are forced to trade time spent with their children for nutrients. And when they still could not manage, their children's chances of nutritional betterment through school meals were stolen by education legislation which abolished minimum nutritional standards. As the food retail industry responded to the changes in income distribution, and moved up-market to chase the purses of the average and better off, those on low wages and benefits became progressively more disadvantaged.

George Orwell said that poverty annihilates the future.[102] It does, literally. In Britain, in 1996, those from the lower socio-economic groups die on average 8 years earlier than the rich.

But poverty also brutalizes. Poverty is a kind of violence. It is offensive to all of us. Rowntree wrote in 1901: 'That in this land of abounding wealth, during a time of perhaps unexampled prosperity, probably more than one quarter of the population are living in poverty is a fact which may well cause great searching of heart. ... no civilization can be sound or stable which has, at its base, this mass of stunted human life. The suffering may well be all but voiceless and we may long remain ignorant of its extent and severity, but when once we realise it, we see that social questions of profound importance await solutions.'[103]

Ninety-five years on, a review of the food poverty crisis today shows how little we have progressed. Trickle-down economics have turned out to be a cruel farce. This is not justice. As one Teesside resident put it:

> 'If you must insist on sticking to the trickle-down economy, let generosity trickle down instead of greed; let truth trickle down instead of closing your eyes to reality; let standing beside your fellow man or woman trickle down instead of bigotry; let hope trickle down instead of suicidal hopelessness, and let love trickle down and the fear of poverty disappear forever.'[104]

References

1   Eliot, G: *Middlemarch*, William Blackwood and Sons, Edinburgh and London, n.d.
2   Walker, C and Church, M: 'Poverty by administration: a review of supplementary benefits, nutrition and scale rates.' *Journal of Human Nutrition* 1978; 32:5-18.
3   Quaker Faith and Practice, from 'We can continue our communion.' Cannon, G in *The Good Fight*, Ebury Press, 1989.
4   Mennell, S: *All Manners of Food*, Blackwell, 1985.
5   ibid.
6   Hoskins, WG: 'Harvest Fluctuations and English Economic History, 1480 -1619', *Agricultural History Review*, 1964, vol. 12; and 'Harvest Fluctuations and English Economic History, 1620 -1750', Agricultural History Review, 1968, vol. 16.
7   Wernham, RB (ed): *The Cambridge Modern History*, vol III, Cambridge University Press, 1968.
8   Nelson, M: 'Social-class trends in British diet', chapter 7, in *Food, Diet and Economic Change Past and Present*, ed Geissler and Oddy, Leicester University Press, 1993.
9   ibid.
10   Ministry of Agriculture, Fisheries and Food: *National Food Survey*, HMSO, 1994.
11   Stitt, S and Grant, D: *Poverty: Rowntree Revisited*, Avebury, 1993.
12   Mingay, GE: 'The Transformation of Agriculture', in *The Long Debate on Poverty*, Readings 9, Institute of Economic Affairs, 1972.
13   Pember Reeves, M: *Round About a Pound a Week*, G. Bell and Sons Ltd, 1913 (also published by Virago Press, 1994).
14   For a discussion of this point see Rivers, JPW, 'The profession of nutrition – an historical perspective', *Proceedings of the Nutrition Society*

(1979), 38, 225.

15 Department for Education: 'A Brief History of School Milk', n.d.

16 National Dairy Council Information Service: Information Booklet Number 2 (1939).

17 Charlton, J and Quaife, K: 'Trends in diet 1841-1991', draft chapter for OPCS Decennial Supplement Series on trends in adult health in Britain, in press.

18 *The State of the Public Health during Six Years of War*, HMSO, 1946.

19 Nelson, M: op. cit.

20 *Enquiry into Income and Wealth,* chaired by Sir Peter Barclay, Joseph Rowntree Foundation, 1995.

21 Bradshaw, J and Lynes, A: *The implications of current benefit levels for income distribution and living standards, and the implications for both living standards and public expenditure of different uprating policies,* University of York, 1993.

22 Goodman, A and Webb, S: *For Richer, For Poorer,* Institute for Fiscal Studies, 1994.

23 The very poor were not of course the same people throughout the decade. The comparison is not between the same people but between different people at the same point on the income distribution.

24 *Households below Average Income (HBAI), A Statistical Analysis, 1979-1992/93,* Government Statistical Service, HMSO, June 1995, and revised edition October 1995, quoted in *Poverty: the facts,* Child Poverty Action Group, 1996.

25 *In Place of Fear,* Transport and General Workers Union Report, 1994.

26 ibid.

27 *Living with the State,* Institute of Fiscal Studies, 1996.

28 Hills, J: *The Future of Welfare,* Joseph Rowntree Foundation, 1993.

29 Jacobs, M, for The Real World Coalition: *The Politics of the Real World,* Earthscan, 1996.

30 Stitt, S and Grant, D: op. cit.

31 Walker, C and Church, M: op. cit.

32 Nelson, M and Naismith, D: 'The nutritional status of poor children in London', *Journal of Human Nutrition,* 1979, 33, 33-45.

33 Townsend, P, Davidson, N and Whitehead, M: *Inequalities in Health, The Black Report and The Health Divide,* Penguin Books, 1992.

34 ibid.

35 Lang, T et al: *Jam Tomorrow,* Manchester Polytechnic, 1984.

36 Maternity Alliance: *Poverty in Pregnancy: the cost of an adequate diet*

for expectant mothers, Maternity Alliance, 1988.
37   Cole-Hamilton, I and Lang, T: *Tightening Belts: a report on the impact of poverty*, London Food Commission Report 13, 1986.
38   Moore, J: 'The End of the Line for Poverty', speech, 11 May 1989. Quoted in Gilmour, I: *Dancing with Dogma*, Simon and Schuster, 1992.
39   *Deep in Debt. A survey of problems faced by low income families*, National Children's Home, London, 1992.
40   Family Budget Unit, *Modest but Adequate Food Budgets for Six Household Types*, York University, 1992.
41   Cole-Hamilton, I: 'A Review of food patterns amongst lower income groups in the UK', report to the Health Education Authority, unpublished.
42   Gilmour, I: op. cit.
43   An exception is the report of the Variations Sub-Group of the Health of the Nation, *Variations in Health. What can the Department of Health Do?*, Department of Health, 1995: 'It is likely that cumulative differential exposure to health damaging or health promoting physical and social environments is the main explanation for observed variations in health and life expectancy.'
44   Leather, S: *By Bread Alone? Poverty and Diet in Britain Today*, MAFF, (CP (92) 9/8), 1992.
45   Ministry of Agriculture, Fisheries and Food: *The Cost of Healthy Eating*, MAFF, (CP (92) 9/3), 1992.
46   Leather, S: 'Less Money, Less Choice' in *Your Food: Whose Choice?*, ed National Consumer Council, HMSO, 1992.
47   ibid.
48   Leather, S quoted in James Erlichman, 'Sainsbury's "healthy" diet caters for the poor', *The Guardian*, 7 September 1994.
49   Ministry of Agriculture, Fisheries and Food: *Household Food Consumption Expenditure, 1990*, HMSO, 1991.
50   European Parliament, *Nutrition in Europe*, Scientific and Technological Options Assessment Draft Final Report, Brussels, March 1995.
51   National Food Surveys, MAFF, for various years. Calculations by MAFF.
52   Central Statistical Office: *Family Spending, A report of the 1995-96 Family Expenditure Survey*, HMSO, 1996.
53   Kent, J: *There's no such thing as a dragon*, Blackie, 1984.
54   MAFF Press Office, statement to author, 4 July 1996.
55   Department of Health Press Office, statement to author, 3 July 1996.
56   Department of Social Security Press Office, statement to author, 3 July 1996.

57   Beaumont, J: *Total Consumer Satisfaction: developing a comprehensive commitment to meeting the needs and priorities of consumers and society*, Institute of Grocery Distribution, 1996.

58   Social Security Committee, Second Report, *Low Income Statistics: Low Income Families (LIF) 1979-1989*, HMSO, 1993; and Social Security Committee, First Report, *Low Income Statistics: Low Income Families (LIF), 1989-1992*, HMSO, 1995. Quoted in *Poverty: the facts*, Child Poverty Action Group, 1996.

59   The author is grateful to MAFF for this irregular data from National Food Survey, 1993.

60   Nelson, M and Paul, A: 'The nutritive contribution of school dinners and other mid-day meals to the diets of school children', *Human Nutrition: Applied Nutrition*, 1983, 37A.

61   Riches, G: 'Hunger, Food Security and Welfare Policies: Issues and Debates in First World Societies', paper presented to Nutrition Society Summer Meeting, June 1996.

62   Hecht, K and Steinman, E: *Improving Access to Food in Low-income Communities: an Investigation of Three Bay Area Neighborhoods*, California Food Policy Advocates, San Francisco, 1996.

63   Grantham-MacGregor S, Powell C, Walker S: 'Nutritional supplements, stunting and child development.' *Lancet*, 1989, ii: 809 -10.

64   *Statement on the Link Between Nutrition and Cognitive Development in Children*, Center on Hunger, Poverty and Nutritional Policy, Tufts University School of Nutrition, 1994.

65   Key, TJA, Thorogood, M, Appleby, PN and Burr, M, 'Dietary habits and mortality in 11,000 vegetarians and health-conscious people: results of a 17-year follow up', *British Medical Journal*, 1996, 313, 775-779.

66   Central Statistical Office: op cit.

67   Dowler, E and Calvert, C: *Nutrition and diet in lone-parent families in London*, Family Policy Studies Centre, 1995.

68   Leather, S: 'Fruit and vegetables: consumption patterns and health consequences', *British Food Journal*, 1995, 97, 7.

69   Lobstein, T: *The nutrition of women on low income*, The Food Commission, 1991.

70   Quoted in Williams, C and Dowler E: 'Identifying successful local projects and initiatives on diet and low income: a review of the issues', Nutrition Task Force Low Income Project Team Working Paper 2.

71   Benzeval, M, Judge, K and Whitehead, M (eds): *Tackling Inequalities in Health*, King's Fund, 1995.

72   B Jacobson, A Smith, and M Whitehead (eds): *The Nation's Health: A Strategy for the 1990s*, King's Fund, 1991.

73   Wilkinson, R: 'Class mortality differentials, income distribution and trends in poverty 1921-81', *Journal of Social Policy,* 1989, 18 (3): 307-35. Also 'Income distribution and life expectancy', *British Medical Journal* 1992. 304: 165-8. And most lately *Unhealthy Societies: The Afflictions of Inequality,* Routledge, 1996.

74   Wilkinson, R: 'Income Distribution and Life Expectancy', *British Medical Journal,* 1992, 304, 165-8.

75   Marsh, A and McKay, S: *Poor Smokers,* Policy Studies Institute, 1994.

76   'Targeting the Rich and the Poor', Mintel 1995, quoted in *Financial Times,* 12 July 1995.

77   Central Statistical Office: op. cit.

78   Raven, H and Lang, T with Dumonteil, C: *Off Our Trolleys?,* Institute for Public Policy Research, 1995.

79   See *Poor and paying for it: the price of living on a low income,* ed Fyfe, G, Scottish Consumer Council, HMSO, 1994.

80   Cole-Hamilton, I and Lang, T: op. cit.

81   Piachaud, D and Webb, J: *The Price of Food: Missing Out on Mass Consumption,* Suntory-Toyota International Centre for Economics and Related Disciplines (STICERD), London School of Economics, October 1996.

82   Spillius, A: 'Invasion of the category killers', *Observer* (Life magazine), 27 February 1994.

83   Quote from Clive Vaughan, Verdict Research, in Spillius, op. cit.

84   Tim Lang's phrase.

85   Dreze, J and Sen, A: *Hunger and Public Action,* Clarendon Press, Oxford, 1989.

86   Distributive justice means the just distribution of goods and property; contrasting with (for instance) procedural, criminal or corrective justice.

87   Low Income Project Team: *Low Income, food, nutrition and health: strategies for improvement,* Department of Health, 1996.

88   *Observer,* 21 January 1996.

89   'Provision, special supplement in support of the IGD's Social Action Programme', *The Grocer,* 8 April 1995.

90   Corporate Intelligence, 'UK Retail Report', in *The Independent,* 19 August 1996.

91   LIPT Report: op. cit.

92   Riches, G: op. cit.

93   Toronto Food Policy Council, 'Reducing urban hunger in Ontario: policy responses to support the transition from food charity to food security.' Toronto Food Policy Council Discussion Paper Series No 1,

December 1994.

94 *SuperMarketing*, 26 July 1996.
95 Wright, CM, Aynsley-Green, A, Tomlinson, P, Ahmed, L and Mac-Farlane, JA: 'A comparison of height, weight and head circumference of primary school children living in deprived and non-deprived circumstances', from *Early Human Development,* 1992, 31, 157-162
96 Wright, CM, Waterson, A and Aynsley-Green, A: 'Effect of deprivation on weight gain in infancy', *Acta Paediatr,* 1994, 83: 357-9.
97 Estimate of unclaimed benefit 1993/94 from *Poverty: the facts,* CPAG, 1996.
98 Food trade deficit figure from MAFF.
99 Tony Blair reported in *Sunday Times,* quoted in *Progress,* Progress Political Education Trust, 1996.
100 Joan Bavaria quoted by New Economics Foundation, 1996.
101 Gilmour, I: op. cit.
102 Orwell, G: *Down and Out in Paris and London,* Victor Gollancz, 1933.
103 Rowntree BS: *Poverty: A Study of Town Life,* Macmillan, 1901.
104 Witness from Teeside to the Church Action on Poverty hearing in the north of England, 19 March 1996.

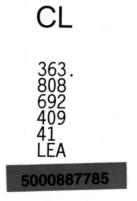